SUPERPOWERS!

A BOOK OF COMPLETELY, TRULY, UTTERLY SUPER THINGS

ABOUT:

....

....

....

OH, IT'S YOU!

Thank goodness you're here!

Because we need you.
Actually, the whole world needs you.
And we need you to turn on
your superpowers.

"Superpowers?" you say,
"I HAVE SUPERPOWERS?"

OF COURSE YOU DO!
And you should use them whenever
you can—because good things
happen when you do.

What kinds of good things? You become even more YOU:
more WONDERFUL, more UNIQUE,
more of everything that makes you special.

And that is a very good thing.
For you. For the world.
FOR EVERYONE.

Because you're the only YOU the world has.
So we need you and your superpowers. Every day.

READY TO GET STARTED?

We sure hope so.

What does it feel like when you are you?

Not **KIND OF** you, not **SORT OF** you, but **REALLY YOU.** Truly **YOU.**

CIRCLE the words that feel like you, and **ADD** some of your own!

FIERCE

KIND

SMART

STRONG

CREATIVE

SILLY

GENTLE

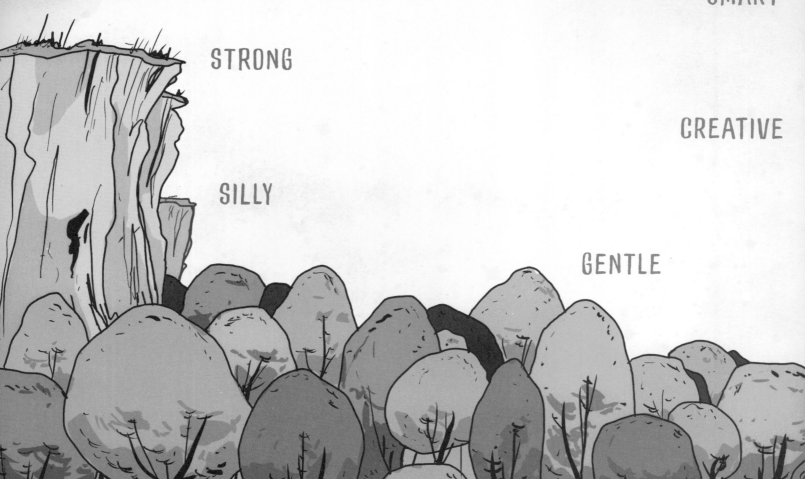

Take a deep breath and sit still for a moment. Pay close attention to what it feels like to be you INSIDE. Through and through.

What makes you so amazing?
What makes you really you?

HELPFUL

WISE

BRAVE

QUIET

DARING

BY THE WAY, I also want you to know that I am:

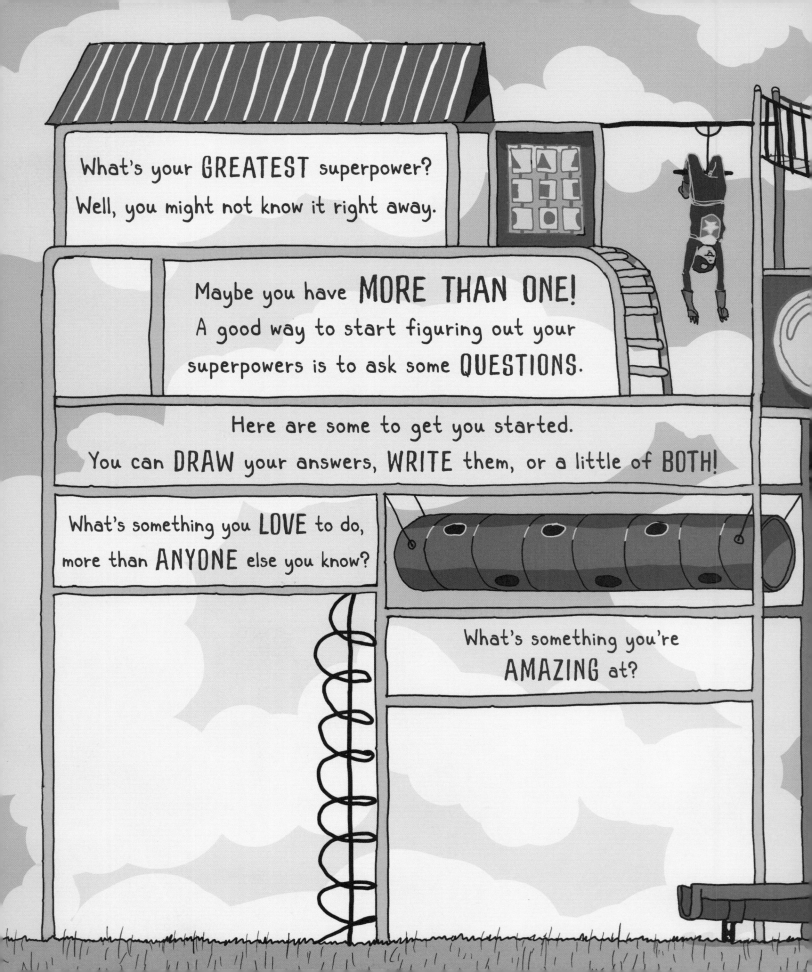

What's your GREATEST superpower?
Well, you might not know it right away.

Maybe you have MORE THAN ONE!
A good way to start figuring out your
superpowers is to ask some QUESTIONS.

Here are some to get you started.
You can DRAW your answers, WRITE them, or a little of BOTH!

What's something you LOVE to do,
more than ANYONE else you know?

What's something you're
AMAZING at?

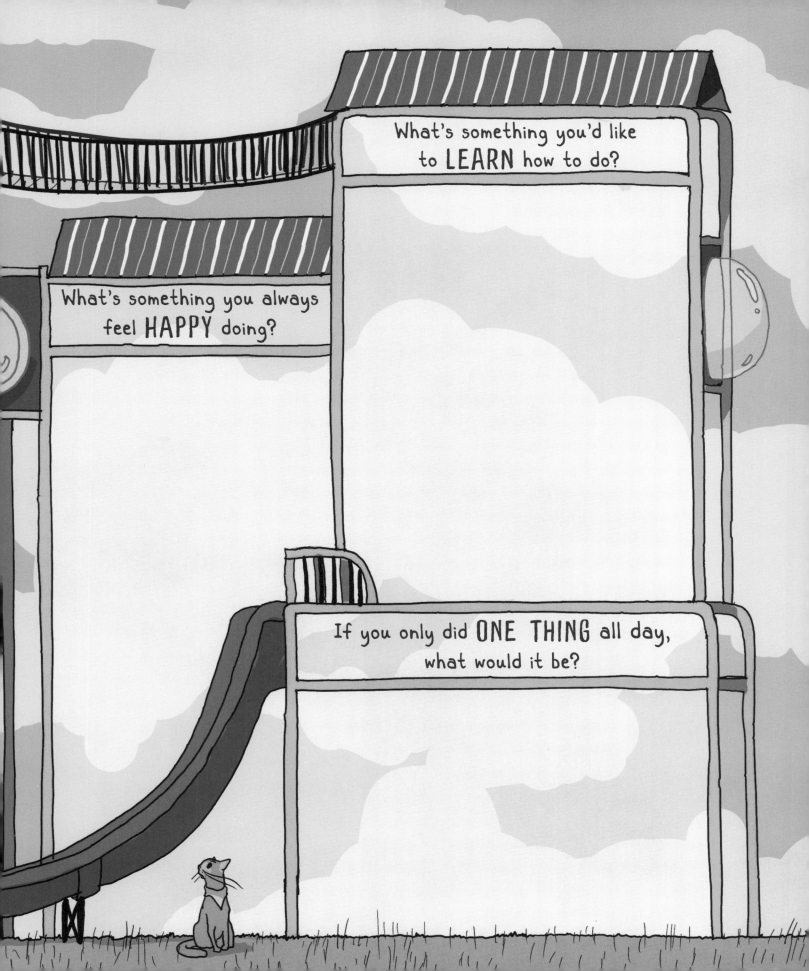

Discovering your superpowers means discovering
some of the most YOU things about you.
Because your superpowers want you to be most like yourself.
This isn't about being someone who YOU AREN'T—
it's about being really who YOU ARE.

So tell us what
makes you so very,
fantastically,
wonderfully

YOU.

I'M THE ONLY PERSON I KNOW WHO LIKES TO ....

NO ONE ELSE .... MORE THAN I DO.

I AM THE MOST .... PERSON I KNOW.

NONE OF MY FAMILY OR FRIENDS .... BUT I DO.

Your family and your friends know
a LOT of GREAT things about you.

So they might have their own IDEAS about
what your SUPERPOWERS might be!
ASK them to write down any superpowers
they think you might have—right here on this page.

Do you AGREE with what they think?
Circle the answers that feel TRUEST for you.

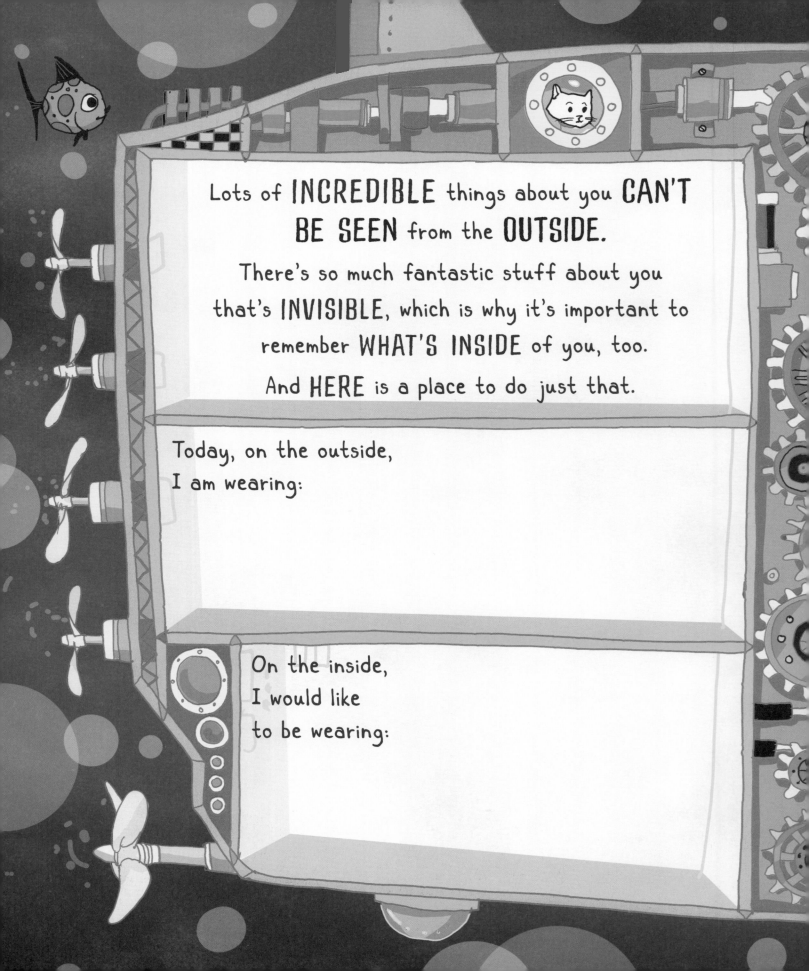

Lots of **INCREDIBLE** things about you **CAN'T BE SEEN** from the **OUTSIDE.**

There's so much fantastic stuff about you that's **INVISIBLE,** which is why it's important to remember **WHAT'S INSIDE** of you, too.

And **HERE** is a place to do just that.

Today, on the outside,
I am wearing:

On the inside,
I would like
to be wearing:

From the outside,
you might think I'm:

On the inside, I'm actually:

From the outside, I look:

On the inside, I feel:

From the outside, people do not
usually guess that I am really:

These pages are here to remind you of some of the **ASTONISHING** things you didn't used to be able to do, but **NOW** you can.

Think back to who you were a **YEAR** ago, **TWO** years ago, even **THREE**. Is there something you've learned how to do or something you've **LEARNED** to be?

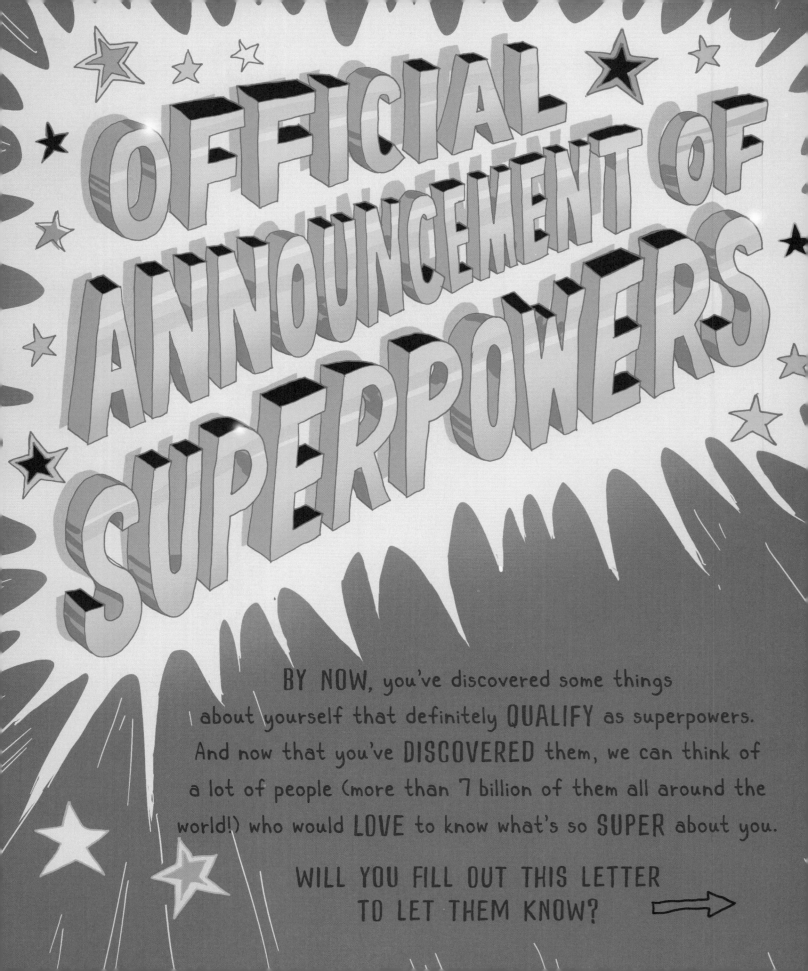

OFFICIAL ANNOUNCEMENT OF SUPERPOWERS

BY NOW, you've discovered some things about yourself that definitely QUALIFY as superpowers. And now that you've DISCOVERED them, we can think of a lot of people (more than 7 billion of them all around the world!) who would LOVE to know what's so SUPER about you.

WILL YOU FILL OUT THIS LETTER TO LET THEM KNOW? ⟹

DEPARTMENT OF SUPERPOWERS ★ ★

Hey, world!

Some of you don't know me already, so I want to tell you my name is:

_____

And I am hereby announcing that one of my greatest superpowers (so far) is:

_____

I am also really good at:

_____

_____

And in my spare time, I want to do more:

_____

_____

And anytime you're feeling like your superpowers need a BOOST, you can come here and TAKE A SIP.

This MAGIC BOTTLE is full of a potion that helps your superpowers GROW STRONGER.

FILL it up with COLORS that will help your POWERS come back to you.

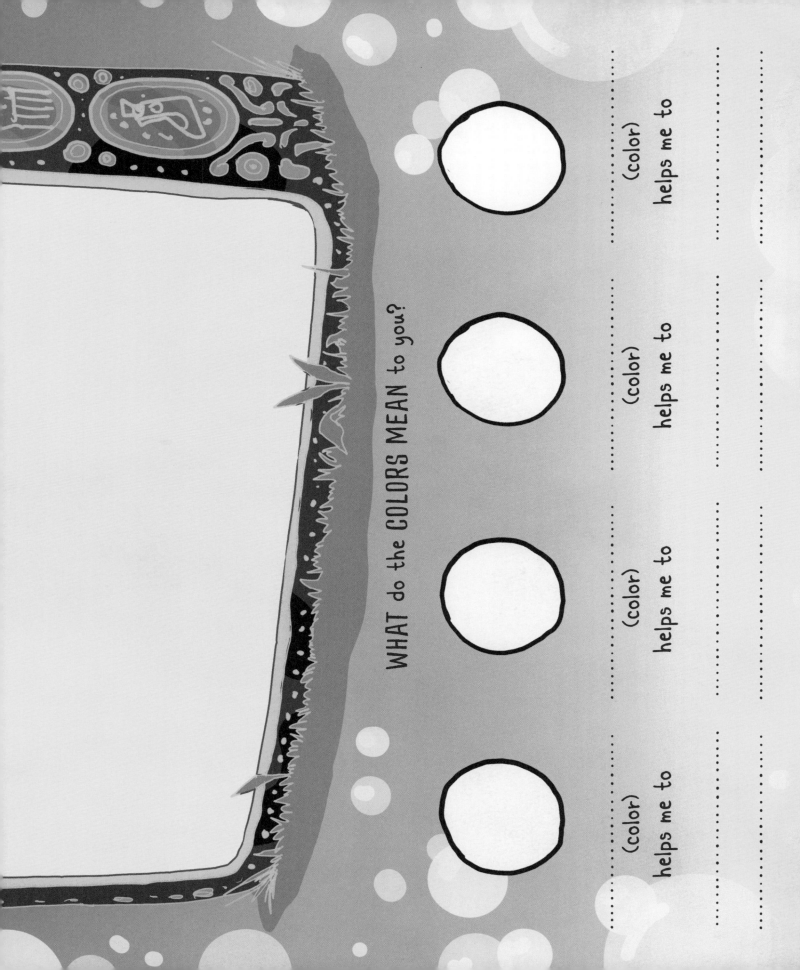

WHAT do the COLORS MEAN to you?

(color)
helps me to

(color)
helps me to

(color)
helps me to

(color)
helps me to

You can be GOOD at a lot of things, but NO ONE in the world is good at EVERYTHING.

It's OKAY to have things you don't want to do, things you aren't interested in, and things you think are pretty boring (okay, maybe even VERRRRRY boring).

If you like, you can think of these as your ANTI-SUPERPOWERS. Everyone has them!

I TRIED, but I just don't like to ....

....

....

....

....

.... is one of my LEAST favorite things to do.

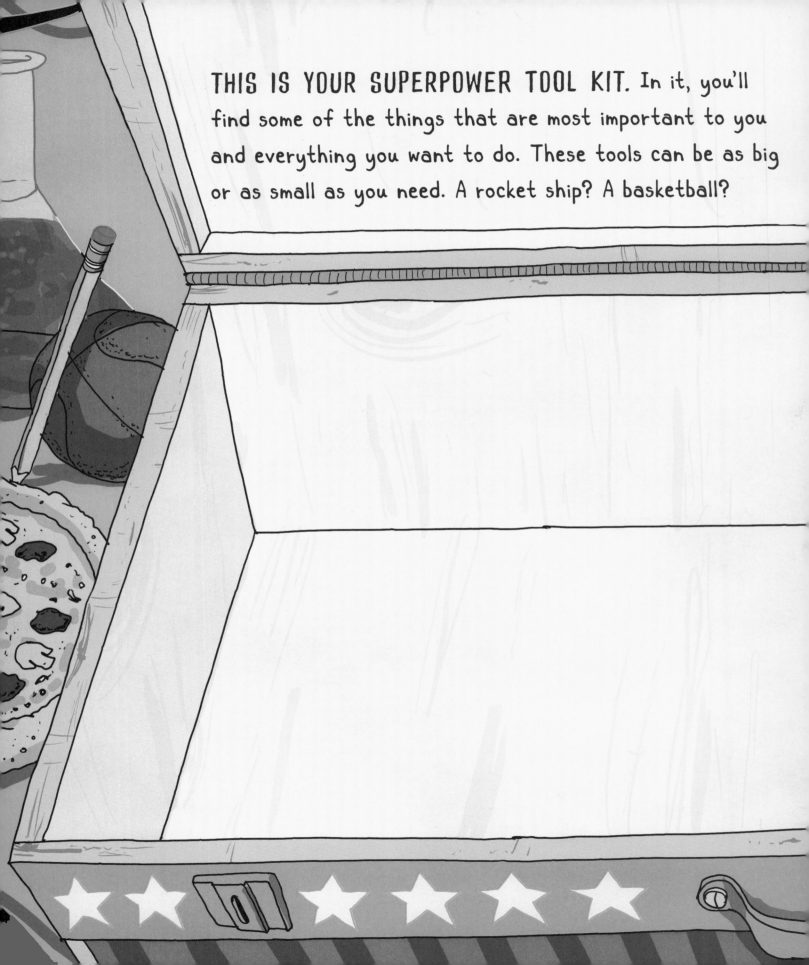

THIS IS YOUR SUPERPOWER TOOL KIT. In it, you'll find some of the things that are most important to you and everything you want to do. These tools can be as big or as small as you need. A rocket ship? A basketball?

A pizza, a parachute, or maybe nothing but a pencil? Fill up your Superpower Tool Kit with EVERYTHING you need to be extremely YOU and everything you need to help you make your superpowers as STRONG as they can be.

DRAW your PERFECT place right here
so you can visit it ANYTIME you like!

You've done something
TRULY INCREDIBLE with your
SUPERPOWERS, and the **WORLD**
has given you this trophy to
CELEBRATE.

Write what you've **DONE**
on the bottom of the trophy,
and add **COLOR** and **DESIGNS**
until this award is everything
you **WANT** it to be.

IF I HAD SUPERPOWER GLASSES, THEY WOULD LOOK LIKE THIS:

Y

X

X

And this is what they would allow me to do:

Y

Made on:	
Name:	
Used for:	

IF I HAD SUPERPOWER SHOES, THEY WOULD LOOK LIKE THIS:

And this is what they would allow me to do:

Made on:	
Name:	
Used for:	

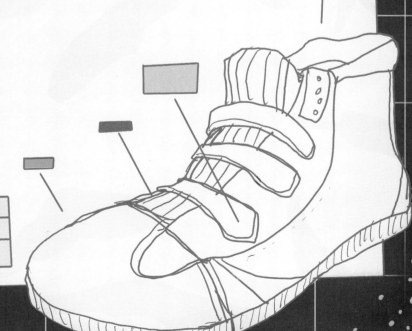

A LEGEND IS THE STORY OF HOW SOMETHING CAME TO BE.

And, though parts of it can be true, there's usually a lot of IMAGINATION involved.

If you were to come up with a wild, incredible STORY of how your superpowers came to be, what would you say?

Check one answer for each question to create a SUPERPOWER LEGEND that's all your own.

Where did your superpowers come from?

☐ outer space ☐ a magic potion

☐ a spell someone cast ☐ I was born with it

When the world first realized you had your superpowers, how did they react?

☐ at first, they were afraid ☐ they threw me a parade

☐ they asked me to help with a very important project (what was it?)

☐ they gave me a gift to thank me (ooh, what did they give you?)

In order to develop your superpowers further, what did you do?

☐ I studied with a famous person (who were they?)

☐ I lived in a special place (where was it?)

☐ I practiced very hard

☐ I got some help from someone I know

How does your story end?

☐ I helped make the world a better place (thanks! what did you do?)

☐ I am developing a new superpower (what is this new superpower?)

☐ I have discovered I can also do something else that's incredible (tell us more!)

☐ I am working on a very important project (exciting! what is it?)

This crystal ball is ready to show you a WONDERFUL thing that's going to happen someday. To you.

It's an INCREDIBLE MOMENT, and it has something to do with your superpowers.

Maybe you're meeting someone really important. Maybe you're doing something INCREDIBLE. Maybe you've ACCOMPLISHED something no one has EVER done before.

DRAW this MAGICAL MOMENT here, so you'll RECOGNIZE it when it HAPPENS!

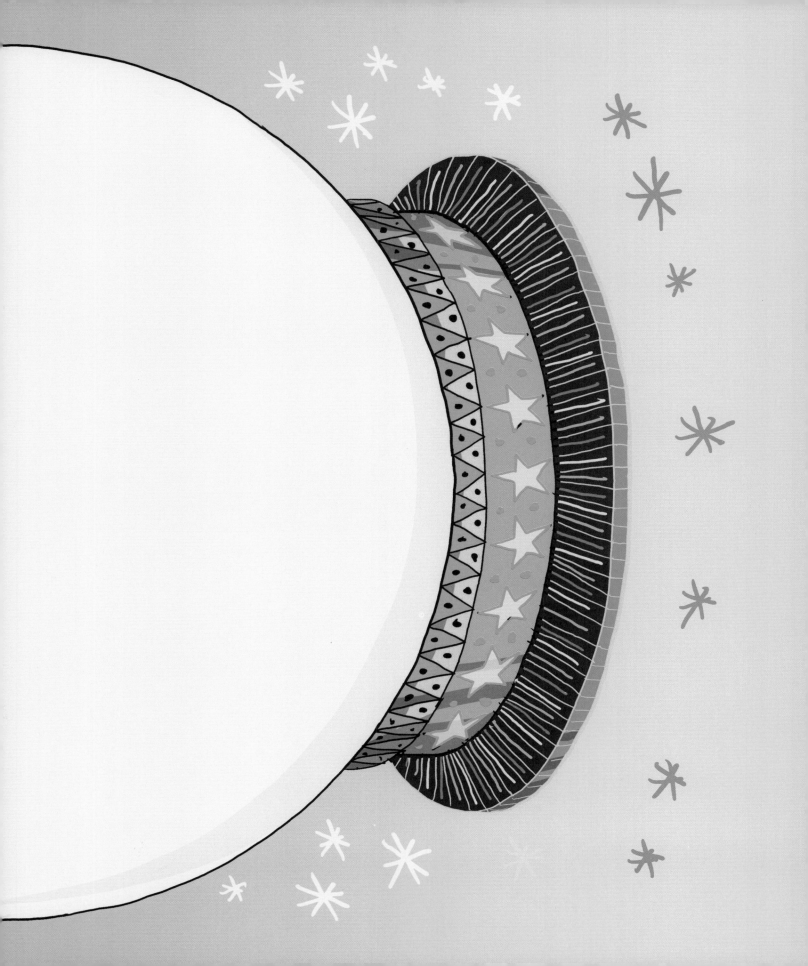

WITH SPECIAL THANKS

TO THE ENTIRE COMPENDIUM FAMILY.

Written by: M.H. Clark

Illustrated by: Michael Byers

Art Direction by: Megan Gandt Guansing

Edited by: Ruth Austin

ISBN: 978-1-943200-75-7

2nd printing. Printed in China with soy inks. A091809002